Disney

GRAVITY FALLS

Lost Legends   by Alex Hirsch

WRITER
ALEX HIRSCH

ARTISTS

JOE PITT

IAN WORREL

ASAF HANUKA

DANA TERRACE

JACOB CHABOT

JIM CAMPBELL

KYLE SMEALLIE

MEREDITH GRAN

MIKE HOLMES

PRISCILLA TANG

SERINA HERNANDEZ

STEPHANIE RAMIREZ

VALERIE HALLA

EDITOR
ERIC GERON

DESIGNER
LINDSAY BRODERICK

LETTERER
CHRIS DICKEY

With special thanks to Dr. Comics & Mr. Games

Artist Breakdown of Work:
JOE PITT: Cover inks; IAN WORREL: Cover paints;
ASAF HANUKA: Inks and paints for pages 42, 54–60; DANA TERRACE: Inks for pages 107–141;
JACOB CHABOT: Inks and paints for pages 50–51; JIM CAMPBELL: Paints for pages 7–39, 107–141; KYLE SMEALLIE: Inks for pages 41–49, 69–71;
MEREDITH GRAN: Pencils for pages 3–6, 40–49, 69–72, 106, 142–144; MIKE HOLMES: Inks for pages 3–6, 40, 72, 106, 142–144;
PRISCILLA TANG: Inks for pages 7–39, 52–53; SERINA HERNANDEZ: Inks and paints for pages 73–105;
STEPHANIE RAMIREZ: Inks and paints for pages 60–68; VALERIE HALLA: Paints for pages 3–6, 40–49, 69–72, 106, 142–144.

Printed in the United States of America
First Hardcover Edition, July 2018
1 3 5 7 9 10 8 6 4 2
FAC-038091-18159
ISBN 978-1-368-04211-6

SUSTAINABLE FORESTRY INITIATIVE Certified Sourcing
www.sfiprogram.org
SFI-00993
Logo Applies to Text Stock Only

AND I HAVE OPINIONS.

LOOSE ENDS THAT I WOULD LIKE TO SEE TIED UP!

AND CERTAIN CHARACTERS WHO I THINK SHOULD BE WITH OTHER CHARACTERS... ROMANTICALLY.

I THINK ABOUT IT DAY AND NIGHT.

IT TORMENTS ME.

NO MATTER! THIS ISN'T ABOUT THAT.

TONIGHT I AM HERE TO BRING YOU LOST TALES, FORBIDDEN ADVENTURES FROM THE PAST THAT ARE YET UNTOLD!

FOR YOUR CURIOSITY, I HAVE ASSEMBLED THESE VARIOUS *CONTENTS* HERE ON THIS *TABLE*.

THIS... SHALL I SAY...

MABEL, THIS IS AMAZING! FINALLY, I HAVE ALL THREE JOURNALS! ACCORDING TO THIS, FORD ONCE DATED A SIREN!

WOWIE ZOWIE! PARANORMAL RASHES! THIS WAS SURE WORTH THE WAIT!

DING DONG

IS THAT YOUR FRIENDS?

DING DONG

DING DONG

DON'T THINK SO... GRENDA USUALLY HEAD-BUTTS THE DOOR.

WHOA! PACIFICA, MY FAVORITE FRENEMY! OR IS IT ENEM-FRIEND?

HEH...LONG TIME NO SEE, PACIFICA! ANY MORE GHOSTS TRY TO MURDER YOU THIS WEEK?

I WISH, DIPPER. IT'S SO MUCH WORSE!

I GOT MY FIRST WRINKLE!

LOOK!

SNRKK

HA-HA!

IT'S NOT FUNNY!

OUR ANNUAL NORTHWEST FAMILY MAGAZINE COVER SHOOT IS TOMORROW.

BETTER FAMILIES THAN YOURS

EVER SINCE THE HAUNTING AT NORTHWEST MANOR, I'VE BEEN ON THIN ICE WITH MOM AND DAD.

I NEED TO LOOK *PERFECT* FOR THIS YEAR'S PHOTO OR THEY'LL CUT OFF ONE OF MY SIX CREDIT CARDS!

PACIFICA, WRINKLES ARE NOTHING TO BE AFRAID OF!

THINK OF THEM AS FRIENDS WHO LIVE ON YOUR FACE AND WILL EVENTUALLY COVER YOU UNTIL YOU'RE DEAD.

YOU DON'T UNDERSTAND...

FIRST IT'S ONE WRINKLE, THEN ANOTHER...

AND BEFORE YOU KNOW IT, YOU LOOK LIKE...

WELCOME TO YOUR FUTURE, SWEETHEART!

TILT

AUGH!!

YEP.

YES, OBVIOUSLY.

I WAS TRYING TO STEAL HERS, BUT A FACE IS A FACE, I SUPPOSE.

POOF!

CAN'T BE TOO PICKY IN THIS MARKET.

THANKS FOR SUMMONING ME, BY THE WAY.

MY WORK HERE IS DONE!

GUYS, HELP ME! I'VE NEVER BEEN IN A MONSTER'S PURSE, AND I DON'T WANT TO START NOW!

AU REVOIR!

FWOOSH

PACIFICA! THIS IS ALL YOUR FAULT!

I TOLD YOU NOT TO TOUCH THAT JOURNAL!

I'M SORRY! NORTHWESTS ARE NATURALLY GOOD AT LYING. IT'S HARD TO TURN IT OFF!

WHAT DO WE DO? HOW DO WE FIND THAT MONSTER?!

My face can see out his bag! He's running towards Main street! Whaaaat!!

MABEL, STAY RIGHT HERE!

WE'RE GOING TO HUNT DOWN THAT CREEP AND GET BACK YOUR FACE!

ON THE BRIGHT SIDE, THOUGH, YOUR SKIN *IS* SUPER SMOOTH...

AUGGHH!

UHH... WE'RE...UH...

UM, ISN'T IT OBVIOUS?!

I'M JACKIE THE ELF-BANDIT, AND THIS IS MY SERVANT, TROLL BOY.

I'M HERE TO SELL HIM INTO INDENTURED SERVITUDE.

WHAT?!

QUIET, TROLL BOY!

YANK!

SERVANTS, AM I RIGHT?

HO-HO! YOU'RE ALL RIGHT, BANDIT JACKIE.

AND I LOVE THE GARBAGE ON YOUR FACE! SO WHAT CAN I DO FOR YOU?

MY SERVANT HERE'S LOOKING FOR REPLACEMENT BODY PARTS. FOR OBVIOUS REASONS.

I MEAN, LOOK AT HIS ABNORMALLY LARGE HEAD.

IT'S *NOT* ABNORMALLY LARGE!

DID YOU SAY *"BODY PARTS"*?!

LIMBY JIMMY'S THE NAME, AND APPENDAGES ARE MY GAME!

LEND ME YOUR EAR AND I'LL LEND YOU A HAND!

BUT IT'LL COST YOU AN ARM AND A LEG!

WACKA WACKA!

Limby Jimmy

UGH, WE DON'T NEED *PUNS*, WE NEED *FACES*!

I MAKE PUNS BECAUSE I'M DEEPLY INSECURE! YUK YUK!

IF YOU WANT FACES, TALK TO *THAT* GUY!

A *FACE* WITH A *CHIN*! NOW SHANDRA WILL REMOVE THAT RESTRAINING ORDER FOR SURE!

PLEASURE DOING BUSINESS WITH YOU.

THAT'S HIM!!

MY MOM IS A TROPHY WIFE.

LITERALLY... MY DAD WON HER IN A YACHTING COMPETITION.

"SHE ALWAYS TAUGHT ME THAT BEAUTY WAS EVERYTHING."

AND THE UGLY DUCKLING NEVER MADE ANY FRIENDS, BECAUSE HIS FACE WAS WEIRD.

THE END.

WAIT, AREN'T THERE MORE PAGES?

NOPE!

RRIIP!

ENJOY YOUR BEAUTY SLEEP—YOU'VE GOT A PAGEANT TOMORROW!

"MY MOM ALWAYS SAID PEOPLE JUDGE A BOOK BY ITS COVER."

I NEED MY COVER, DIPPER.

BECAUSE WITHOUT IT... I'M NOT SURE WHO I REALLY AM.

PREPARE TO BE DESTROY—

ZAP!

ACKK

UNCLE *FORD!*

STAN CALLED ME WHEN HE FOUND YOUR SISTER LIKE THIS.

IT'S A GOOD THING I'M GREAT AT CHARADES.

I'VE BEEN TRYING TO FIND THAT MARKET FOR YEARS!

AND IT LOOKS LIKE I HAVE A NEW SPECIMEN FOR THE BUNKER. NICELY DONE, KIDS!

WHOO BOY, IT IS *GREAT* TO GET THE BAND BACK TOGETHER!

AND SO PACIFICA LEARNED THAT BEAUTY IS ONLY SKIN DEEP, AND DIPPER LEARNED THAT THE BEST PLACE FOR ROMANCE IS TRAPPED INSIDE A BURLAP SACK.

SPEAKING OF WHICH, I "INTERCEPTED" THIS TEXT EXCHANGE BETWEEN THE TWO OF THEM AFTERWARDS AND I FOUND IT INTERESTING.

VERY INTERESTING.

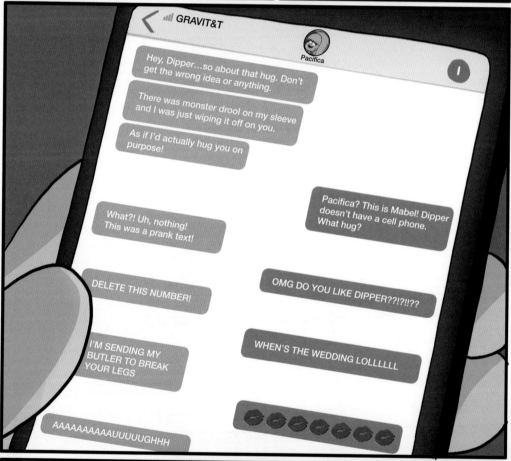

GRAVIT&T

Pacifica

Hey, Dipper...so about that hug. Don't get the wrong idea or anything.

There was monster drool on my sleeve and I was just wiping it off on you.

As if I'd actually hug you on purpose!

Pacifica? This is Mabel! Dipper doesn't have a cell phone. What hug?

What?! Uh, nothing! This was a prank text!

DELETE THIS NUMBER!

OMG DO YOU LIKE DIPPER??!?!!??

I'M SENDING MY BUTLER TO BREAK YOUR LEGS

WHEN'S THE WEDDING LOLLLLLL

AAAAAAAAAAAUUUUUGHHH

HO-HO! UNCOMFORTABLE. ANYWAY, IF YOU THINK *THAT* SEEMS SKETCHY, PREPARE YOURSELF FOR OUR *NEXT STORY*...

ABUELITA'S FILLING MY STORAGE CLOSET WITH HER CREEPY PORCELAIN ANGELS, SO I NEED A NEW PLACE TO KEEP MY *COMIC COLLECTION!*

ENJOY, DUDES!

WHOA, ADOLESCENT POWER FANTASIES!

PRETTY MEN IN PRETTIER TIGHTS!

AND WITH A LITTLE WHITE-OUT...

YOU CAN FIX THE BORING DIALOGUE!

EGAD! MY FACE IS 90% CHIN!

I'LL NEVER *PUNCH AWAY* MY LONELINESS!

HAHA! EISNER AWARD, HERE I COME!

BAH!

SO-CALLED *COMIC BOOKS* ARE DUMB RAGS FOR BABIES AND THE PERPETUALLY UNEMPLOYED!

SOOS! LOAD THESE INTO THE *BOTTOMLESS PIT!*

BUT, MR. PINES, COMICS ARE A LEGITIMATE ARTISTIC MEDIUM!

LIKE EASTER EGG PAINTING OR RODEO CLOWNING!

BALDERDASH! WORDS AND PICTURES ARE AN UNHOLY UNION!

BESIDES, THESE GOOF-'EM-UP RAGS JUST DISTRACT THE EMPLOYEES! LOOK!

HAHA, OH, *BLARCHIE!*

BLARCHIE

WHO NEEDS A PERSONALITY WHEN YOU HAVE FRECKLES!

THAT'S IT!

I'M HIDING THESE WACKY PAGES BEFORE THEY CONVINCE YOU TO GO TO ART SCHOOL!

HEY!

BOO!

MY COMICS! WHAT WILL I COMPLAIN ABOUT ONLINE NOW?

I'LL JUST HIDE 'EM IN FORD'S HORRIFYING OLD CHEST.

NO ONE WOULD EVER OPEN THIS NIGHTMARE!

CREAK

THERE'S NO WAY THIS COULD IRONICALLY BACKFIRE!

SLAM!

I'M FINALLY FREE FROM COMICS!

OR *WAS* HE...?

ANOTHER DAY FINDS GRUNKLE STAN SCRATCHING HIMSELF, PANTSLESS AND ALONE!

DUCKTECTIVE... YOU'RE PREGNANT?! *QUACK QUACK*

SCRATCH SCRATCH

STAN PAN

WHAT THE—WHAT IS THAT YELLOW BOX?

STAN IS VEXED BY THE NARRATION! BUT ALAS, HE IS TOO DUMB TO DO ANYTHING ABOUT IT!

HEY! CUT THAT OUT!

CAN IT, WISE GUY!

WHOOSH

STAN SWIPES BUT IS TOO SLOW TO STOP THE BOX! IS THIS THE END OF OUR *HERO*?

I'LL TEACH YOU TO OMNISCIENTLY NARRATE *ME*!

HAHAHAHA!

LATER, DOWN IN THE LAB...

THIS DUMB BOX WON'T STOP NARRATING ME!

AND IT KEEPS USING OBNOXIOUS WORDS LIKE *"ZOUNDS"* AND *"MEANWHILE"*!

HMMM...

YOU'RE CLEARLY UNDER SOME KIND OF CURSE.

DID YOU INSULT ANYONE LATELY?

OH SURE, A NUN, SOME GIRL SCOUTS, THE ENTIRE HOUSE OF REPRESENTATIVES, AND SOOS'S DUMB COMICS. BUT I LOCKED THOSE IN YOUR OLD CHEST IN THE CLOSET.

STAN, THAT CHEST IS CURSED!

IS *EVERYTHING* YOU OWN CURSED?!

MOMENTS LATER...

CREEEAAAAK

DIPPER 'n' PALS

WE'RE IN. NOW START LOOKING FOR STANLEY AND *DON'T TOUCH ANYTHING!*

THUD!

THIS IS SO WEIRD— WE'RE STUCK IN TINY *BOXES.*

THIS MUST BE HOW MIMES FEEL *ALL THE TIME!*

CHECK IT OUT, DAWGS! I MADE A *THWOCK!*

THWOCK!

COOL! TWO HATS!

WHAT? *HEY!*

I GUESS I SHOULD HAVE SEEN THAT COMING.

BE CAREFUL! THIS WORLD IS SUBJECTIVE AND UNSTABLE AND COULD *CHANGE STYLES* AT ANY MOMENT!

ZAP!

HO-**HO**! **NOW** WE'RE **TALKING**! WHAT IS THIS PLACE?

THIS IS **THE GRIMDARK CHRONICLES**, A COMIC WHERE EVERYONE YOU LIKE DIES. IT'S VERY POPULAR!

IT'S LIKE WE'RE INSIDE DIPPER'S BRAIN!

YOU THERE! HAVE YOU SEEN A POINTY MAN WITH A FEDORA AND NO RESPECT FOR THE LAWS OF PHYSICS?

NYAAARRRRGHHHH*

*I CAN'T SEE MUCH, PAL! THESE PAGES ARE 80% PURE BLACK!

I HAVE SEEN THE MAN YOU SEEK. CAW! HE WENT IN THROUGH THOSE CATACOMBS. CAW!

THANKS, TERRIFYING BIRD! I TRUST YOU 100%!

COOL! SILHOUETTES!

I THINK WE'RE GETTING CLOSE—THIS COULD BE IT!

I'M STICKING OUT MY TONGUE RIGHT NOW, BUT YOU CAN'T SEE!

THIS METAL FIST IS CHAFING, GUYS!

THUD

?

OH, NO—
I'VE BEEN
BLOWN INTO THE
MARGINS! DUDES?
DUDES, WHERE
ARE YOU?!

OH, MAN,
THIS IS CONFUSING.
A "D" THAT LOOKS
LIKE A "G"?
WHERE AM I?

SOOS! UH... I WASN'T CRYING! I WAS SHOOTING *ATTACK POISON* FROM MY EYES! LIKE A DESERT LIZARD! STAY BACK!

THIS IS WHERE YOU'VE BEEN? I'VE NEVER SEEN THIS COMIC BEFORE.

THAT'S BECAUSE *LIL' STANLEY* IS *MY* COMIC. I DREW IT MYSELF WHEN I WAS 10 YEARS OLD!

BUT I THOUGHT YOU HATED COMICS!

I...I...

KNUCKLE SANDWICH

I LOVED COMICS, SOOS!!!

"I READ THEM ALL! *CAPTAIN NAZI-PUNCHER! SKIMPARELLA! THE X-CESSIVE FORCE!* CREATING MY OWN COMIC WAS MY CHILDHOOD DREAM!

"WHILE STANFORD WAS RECITING THE DIGITS OF PI IN HIS SLEEP, I WAS PLANNING A CARTOON EMPIRE!

"BUT I WAS REJECTED BY PUBLISHERS. THEY SAID *LIL' STANLEY* CONTAINED TOO MUCH 'SWEARING' FOR KIDS AND WAS 'TECHNICALLY A PYRAMID SCHEME IN COMIC FORM.'

"I GAVE UP ON PUNCH LINES AND INSTEAD JUST TOOK UP PUNCHING IN GENERAL. I WAS A CARTOONIST NO MORE!"

I ALSO GOT IN A FISTFIGHT WITH STAN LEE IN 1973, WHICH DIDN'T HELP THINGS. THAT'S WHY I CAN'T BEAR TO SEE COMICS NOW.

I *LOVED* COMICS, SOOS... BUT COMICS NEVER LOVED ME BACK.

HEY, YOU!

LIL' STANLEY FOR SALE! ONLY THREE BUCKS!

I AM INDIFFERENT TO TUESDAYS.

I'M GONNA POISON YOUR LASAGNA, SARCASTI-PUP!

SASS

DUDE, ALL THIS TIME YOU WERE A FELLOW COMIC LOVER LIKE ME! WE HAVE SO MUCH TO DISCUSS—SECRET IDENTITIES, PLOT TWISTS, CONVENTION ODORS, LETTERING... *LETTERING, DUDE!*

KEEP IT DOWN! I DON'T WANT SARCASTI-PUP TO MAKE FUN OF ME!

HIS THOUGHT BUBBLES CAN BE HURTFULLY SASSY.

GUYS! YOU ESCAPED!

YEAH, I REMEMBERED THIS PLACE IS JUST MADE OUT OF PAPER. IT'S REALLY EASY TO CUT.

PLUS WE REALIZED WE'D NEED TO PAY ANOTHER $14.99 TO BUY THE NEXT ISSUE OF THIS STORY.

$14.99?! THAT'S HIGHWAY ROBBERY! AS A FORMER HIGHWAY ROBBER, I WOULD KNOW!

YOU CAN'T ESCAPE THAT EASY! I'LL JUST KEEP INTRODUCING PLOT TWISTS AND VILLAINS UNTIL YOU'RE DONE FOR, AND THERE'S NOTHING YOU CAN DO TO STOP ME!

OH YEAH?

THIS ENDS... WHITE NOW!

NOT WHITE-OUT! NOOOOOO!! IS THIS THE END OF ME? YES, APPARENTLY!

ZAP

LET THAT BE A LESSON TO ALL OF US.

BENEATH EVERY HARD, GRUNKLEY EXTERIOR BEATS THE SOFT, NERDY HEART OF A SOOS!

WEIRDMAGEDDON: THE AFTERWEIRDNESS

OUR NEXT STORY CONCERNS WEIRDMAGEDDON. ALTHOUGH BILL'S DEMISE REPAIRED THE RIFT, GRAVITY FALLS WAS NEVER QUITE THE SAME AFTER.

A GIANT FAULT LINE (WHICH DIPPER NAMED "MABEL'S FAULT") OPENED UP IN THE FOREST...

PHONE RECEPTION BEGAN GLITCHING...

AND A FEW TINY DIMENSIONAL RIPS REMAINED, POPPING UP IN THE ODDEST PLACES...

FORD DECIDED TO INVITE THE KIDS ALONG ON ONE LAST ADVENTURE TO REPAIR THESE WORMHOLES. UNFORTUNATELY, WHEN ONE RIFT CLOSES, ANOTHER ONE SOMETIMES OPENS... IN A STORY I CALL...

DON'T DIMENSION IT

AH, FINALLY A FAMILY CAMPING TRIP! I'M GOING TO NAME EVERY SQUIRREL AND EAT EVERY DANGEROUS KIND OF OAK!

CHRP CHRP

WE'RE NOT CAMPING, MABEL. THIS IS A SCIENTIFIC EXPEDITION!

WE'RE SEARCHING FOR LEFTOVER MULTIDIMENSIONAL RIPS FROM WEIRDMAGEDDON TO PATCH WITH ALIEN ADHESIVE. SO KEEP AN EYE OUT FOR ANYTHING THAT SEEMS...

LOVECRAFTY.

GREAT-UNCLE FORD, WHAT WAS IT *LIKE* IN THE MULTIVERSE, ANYWAY?

CONFUSING. ONE MINUTE YOU'RE BREATHING AIR, THE NEXT YOU'RE BREATHING FINGERS. THINK YOU FOUND A SANDWICH? IT'S A *PLANET.*

YOU JUST ATE A PLANET.

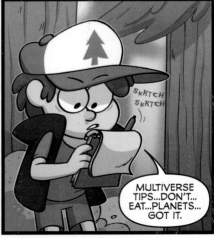

SKRTCH SKRTCH

MULTIVERSE TIPS...DON'T... EAT...PLANETS... GOT IT.

JUST BE CAREFUL WHERE YOU POINT THAT NERD GUN, BRAINIAC!

WE NEED THESE KIDS BACK ON THE BUS IN THREE DAYS, AND I WANT 'EM GOING HOME IN ONE PIECE!

STANLEY, UNDER *YOUR* WATCH THE TWINS FELL INTO A BOTTOMLESS PIT.

I'M NOT SURE *YOU* SHOULD BE GIVING *CARETAKER ADVICE*.

WHAT? I'M THE *BEST CARETAKER EVER!*

I'VE TAUGHT THESE KIDS VALUABLE LIFE LESSONS, LIKE HOW TO HOTWIRE COP CARS!

WHAT'S DIPPER'S REAL NAME?

DIPTHOLOMEW! I DUNNO! BOTTOM LINE, I COULD CARETAKER CIRCLES AROUND YOU!

HEY, GRUNKLE STAN, THIS OAK MAKES MY FACE FEEL FUNNY!

NOT NOW, SWEETIE!

PSSST—
HEY, DIPPER!
GUESS WHO
I BROUGHT
ALONG!

SQUEE!

MABEL, DIDN'T YOU
HEAR FORD? THIS IS
A DANGEROUS
MISSION!

AW, C'MON!
THIS GAL NEEDS
SOME ONE-ON-ONE
PIG TIME BEFORE
SUMMER'S OVER!

MABEL, I KNOW YOU DON'T
WANT TO HEAR THIS, BUT
DON'T YOU THINK YOU'RE
BEING A *PINCH
SELF-CENTERED*?

WHAT!
I'M THE LEAST
SELF-CENTERED
PERSON!

TRUST ME,
IT'S SCIENTIFICALLY
PROVEN THAT EVERY
ADVENTURE IS BETTER
WITH A PIG. RIGHT,
WADDLES?

WADDLES?!

MABEL!

FORD, DO SOMETHING!

GOOD THING I WORE MY INFINITY BELT!

STANLEY, GRAB AHOLD OF ME!

BAD THINGS ARE HAPPENING RIGHT NOW, GUYS!!!

WHATEVER YOU DO, DON'T LET...

GO.

AAAA

MABEL, NO!

RAZZLE MY DAZZLE, IT'S A *MABEL BONANZA!* THERE'S EVERY POSSIBLE VERSION OF ME...

TABLE MABEL...

MOLECULARLY UNSTABLE MABEL...

AND HEY, YOU LOOK JUST LIKE ME!

WHOA, *GIRL,* YOU ARE FIERCE AND I *LOVE* IT.

REEE

HELLO THERE!

YOU MUST BE NEW HERE. WHICH MABEL ARE YOU?

UH, THE **BEST** MABEL, OBVIOUSLY, HAHA!

SLIGHTLY... ARROGANT... MABEL... GOT IT.

WHAT! I'M NOT ARROGANT! I'M LOVABLE! HERE'S A JOKE—HOW MANY MABELS DOES IT TAKE TO SCREW IN A LIGHTBULB?

THAT IS **EXTREMELY** OFFENSIVE TO LIGHTBULB MABEL!

SNIFF...

OH MY GOSH! I AM **SO SORRY**, LIGHTBULB MABEL!

I JUST DON'T UNDERSTAND. WHAT IS THIS PLACE?

ALLOW ME TO EXPLAIN. WHEN SIMILAR BEINGS GET LOST IN THE MULTIVERSE, THEY TEND TO BE DRAWN TO EACH OTHER, CLUSTERING TOGETHER LIKE POTATO CHIP CRUMBS AT THE BOTTOM OF THE BAG.

WELCOME TO DIMENSION MAB-3L, WHERE LOST MABELS STICK TOGETHER!

THANKS, *EXPLAINBEL!* SUPER HELPFUL! BUT LIKE... HOW DO WE GET OUT OF HERE?

UNFORTUNATELY, WE'RE TRAPPED FOREVER.

THE SMARTEST MABEL HERE, *BRAINBEL*, TRIED TO INVENT A DIMENSIONAL ESCAPE POD, BUT SHE'S BEEN TOO BUSY WORKING ON HER STICKER COLLECTION TO FINISH IT.

WHAT?! I MEAN, I LOVE STICKERS AS MUCH AS THE NEXT MABEL, BUT WHAT ABOUT HOME?

I BET IF WE WORKED TOGETHER, WE COULD GET THAT PUPPY UP AND RUNNING!

SORRY, I TOTALLY LOST MY TRAIN OF THOUGHT WHEN YOU SAID *"PUPPY."*

WHO SAID *"PUPPY"*?!

PUPPY? WHERE?

I WANT TO PET A PUPPYYYY!!

MABEL! MABEL, SWEETIE! IF YOU COME OUT, I'VE GOT SOME CANDY FOR YOU!

AND I'LL GIVE YOU SOME DELICIOUS VITAMIN SUPPLEMENTS! 14 KINDS OF ZINC!

YOU DON'T KNOW ANYTHING ABOUT MABEL, DO YOU?

OF COURSE I DO! I SCANNED HER ENTIRE MOLECULAR STRUCTURE THE DAY I CAME HERE.

GUESS HOW MANY ENZYMES SHE HAS. THE ANSWER MIGHT SURPRISE YOU!

SIXER, I SWEAR, IF I LOSE MY NIECE...

STANLEY, TRUST ME, WE'LL FIND MABEL. I KNOW THE MULTIVERSE.

MABEL?

KEEP LOOKING.

PH'NGLUI MGLW'NAFH

BRAINBEL, PLEASE! I HAVE TO GET BACK HOME! I JUST ESCAPED ONE WEIRDMAGEDDON, AND I DON'T NEED ANOTHER ONE!

CHILLAX! SHE'LL GET AROUND TO IT WHENEVS! WANNA HACK SOME SACK?

I DO *NOT* APPRECIATE YOUR *LAID-BACK ATTITUDE,* MABRO!

THESE MABELS ARE DRIVING ME CRAY-BEL! THE STANS CAN'T GET HERE SOON ENOUGH!

FINALLY, A *NORMAL ONE!*

OH, HEY. WHICH MABEL ARE YOU?

THEY HAVEN'T GIVEN ME A NAME YET, THANK GOODNESS.

I DON'T KNOW WHY THEY THINK *EVERYONE* NEEDS ONE.

SOUNDS LIKE YOU'RE *ANTI-LABEL MABEL.*

NO! I'M JUST A **REGULAR MABEL** LIKE YOU!

LISTEN, THERE'S A WAY OUT OF HERE, BUT I DON'T TRUST THESE OTHER WHACK-JOBS TO WORK TOGETHER WITH ME.

SOME OF THESE OTHER MABELS SERIOUSLY CREEP ME OUT!

HEYYY! **STANBEL** IS SINGLE AND READY TO MINGLE!

SHUDDER

YOU'VE GOT FRIENDS SEARCHING FOR YOU, RIGHT? WE NEED TO SEND A **SIGNAL** TO THEM.

MILITARY EXPERT MABEL HAS A FLARE GUN, BUT SHE SAYS IT'S FOR "EMERGENCY RAVES ONLY."

YOU DISTRACT HER, I'LL STEAL IT, AND TOGETHER WE CAN GET BACK TO OUR HOME DIMENSIONS!

I LIKE THE WAY YOU THINK, MABEL!

THAT'S 'CAUSE I THINK LIKE YOU, MABEL!

EEEEEEEHHHH!!

THIS DISTRESS BEACON WILL SUMMON EITHER AN INTERDIMENSIONAL GOOD SAMARITAN OR AN UNIMAGINABLE BEAST THAT FEEDS ON FEAR.

I LIKE THOSE ODDS!

HONK! HONK!

WELL, ENTANGLE MY PARTICLES, WHAT ARE YOU APOSTROPHE BACKSLASHERS DOIN' OUT HERE IN THE MULTI-STICKS?

WE'RE LOOKING FOR THE BEST GRANDNIECE IN THE MULTIVERSE! YA SEEN HER?

MAYBE I HAVE, BUT I'D NEVER LET A KNOWN CRIMINAL ONTO MY TRUCK!

MY CRIMINAL RECORD MADE IT INTO SPACE?! I GOTTA ADMIT, I'M KINDA IMPRESSED WITH MYSELF.

I WAS *TALKING* ABOUT *HIM!* YOUR WANTED POSTERS ARE EVERYWHERE FROM HERE TO LOTTOCRON 9*!*

HAHAHA, YOU SERIOUS?! MR. GOODY NERD-SHOES IS A *CRIMINAL* OUT HERE?!

LOOK, I MIGHT HAVE STOLEN A FEW... HUNDRED...PARTS TO BUILD MY QUANTUM DESTABILIZER, BUT IT WAS ALL IN THE NAME OF SCIENCE!

HOW'S ABOUT WE LEAVE HIM CUFFED IN THE BACK AND I SIT IN THE FRONT?

DEAL*!*

WHAT?!

SO I SAYS, "DARK MATTER? MORE LIKE *DORK* MATTER!"

HAHA! BRILLIANT!

I HATE THIS.

SO THERE I WAS, SURROUNDED BY BODIES. I WON THE WAR BUT I HAD LOST MY SOUL, AND I WAS ALL LIKE...

..."WHAAAAT?!"

OH, TOTALLY. *TOTALLY.* BEEN THERE!

OOH, GOTTA GO. MABEL BIZ.

SIR, YES SIR!

6-18

I HOPE THIS WORKS!

JINX! HAHA! YOU AND ME. WHAT A PAIR WE ARE.

BANG

BOOOM!

THERE SHE IS! QUICK! HEAD TOWARDS THAT EXPLODING CHILD!

WHOOOSH

WE DID IT!

HAHAA! MABELS FOR THE WIN!

GONNA BE A LONG TRIP BACK. NEED A BATHROOM BREAK?

GOOD THINKING, ME! I AM *SO* CONSIDERATE!

BE RIGHT BAAAAAACK!

SLAM!

CA-CHUNK!

HEY, WAIT! WHAT ARE YOU DOING?! FORD'S HERE TO RESCUE US!

CORRECTION— HE'S HERE TO RESCUE *ME!* YOU'RE STUCK HERE, IDIOT!

WHAT?!

YOU THINK I WANT TO BE *TRAPPED* IN THIS GODFORSAKEN *MAB-HOLE* LISTENING TO THESE NITWITS TALK ABOUT BOYS AND GLITTER FOR ALL ETERNITY?! I DON'T EVEN *LIKE* GLITTER!

W-WHAT KIND OF MABEL *ARE* YOU?!

THE EXACT KIND OF MABEL YOU *AREN'T.*

AND CONSIDERING HOW EASY IT WOULD BE FOR ME TO GUESS THIS, *YOU'LL* PROBABLY NEVER FIGURE IT OUT.

YOU'RE... YOU'RE THE EXACT OPPOSITE OF ME!

YOU'RE...

THE ANTI-MABEL!

BANG
BANG
BANG

NO! NO! THIS CAN'T BE HAPPENING!

WHAM!

EVERYONE, QUICK!

WE HAVE TO STOP THAT SHIP OR I'M TRAPPED HERE FOREVER!

TOTALLY. I'LL HELP RIGHT AFTER I FINISH MY COTTAGES. RIGHT, MEOWBEL?

CAN'T TALK. CHASING TAIL.

HA! GO! GO! GO!

WHAT'S **WRONG** WITH YOU GUYS! THIS IS AN *IMPORTANT MISSION* AND YOU'RE JUST ALL BEING *TOTALLY SELF-CENTER—*

OHHH...

OH, MABEL, YOU GOTTA WORK ON YO'SELF.

ATTENTION, MABELS OF MAB-3L! I USED TO BE JUST LIKE YOU: SO CAUGHT UP IN MY OWN MABELNESS THAT I NEGLECTED THOSE AROUND ME!

HECK, I CAUSED AN ENTIRE APOCALYPSE JUST TO GET ONE MORE DAY OF SUMMER!

CRIKEY! YOU GOTTA BE PULLIN' OUR WALLABIES, MATE!

I'M AFRAID IT'S TRUE, G'DAYBEL. I'M GOING TO BE BETTER, BUT IN ORDER TO DO THAT, I NEED TO GET BACK HOME!

MY RIDE IS LEAVING, AND IF YOU HELP ME CATCH IT, I PROMISE I'LL NEVER BE SELFISH AGAIN.

NOW, I KNOW IT'S A LONG SHOT, BUT... *DOES ANYONE HERE HAVE A GRAPPLING HOOK?!*

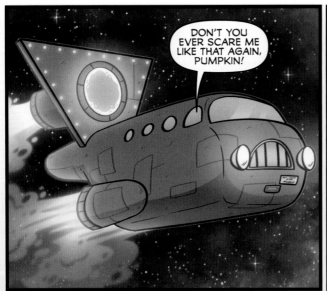

DON'T YOU EVER SCARE ME LIKE THAT AGAIN, PUMPKIN!

APOLOGIES, DEAREST UNCLE. I WILL NOT TRANSGRESS YOUR LAWS AGAIN.

HAHA! *"TRANSGRESS"*! CLASSIC MABEL!

PSST! STANLEY, SOMETHING SEEMS...OFF ABOUT MABEL.

OH, HERE WE GO. YOU'RE JUST JEALOUS THAT I WAS ABLE TO PICK HER OUT OF A CROWD AND YOU WEREN'T!

GREAT-UNCLE STANFORD, DO YOU HAVE ANY FUTURISTIC MEGA-WEAPONS THAT I COULD BRING HOME WITH ME?

FOR EDUCATIONAL PURPOSES?

YES... OVER THERE BY THE AIRLOCK.

MABEL, SWEETIE, I THINK MAYBE YOU'VE HAD TOO MUCH SUGAR—

I'M NOT MABEL!

DANG IT, STAN! YOU GOT THE WRONG ONE!

OH, YOU ARE *LOVING* THE CHANCE TO THROW THIS IN MY FACE!

SOUNDS LIKE YOU TWO NEED SOME SPACE.

ENDLESS SPACE!

RRRRUMMBLE

WHA? WHAT IS THAT?!

BOOOM!

SPLAT!
SPLAT!
SPLAT!

I CAN'T FEEL MY LEGS!

HAD ENOUGH?!

CLANG

YOU! I'LL KNOCK THE GLITTER OUT OF YOU, YOU GIGGLING PUNCH LINE!

I'D LIKE TO SEE YOU TRY.

LOOK! A PUPPY!

WHERE?

MAB-PUNCH!

WHAT'S GOING ON?! WHICH ONE'S THE REAL MABEL?

I CAN'T TELL! THEY'RE EQUALLY ADORABLE!

WELCOME TO *SWEATER TOWN!*

HRKKKKK!

STAN! FORD! SHE'S THE IMPOSTER! TAKE HER OUT!

SHE'S LYING! SHE'S EVIL INCARNATE!

WHY DOES THIS *ALWAYS HAPPEN* WITH DOUBLES?!

IF THERE WAS ONLY SOME WAY TO TELL THEM APART!

WHIP!

WAIT... WAIT...IT'S NOT WHAT IT LOOKS LIKE!

YOU THINK YOU'VE DEFEATED ME, BUT I'M PART OF YOU!

EVERY SELFISH CHOICE YOU MAKE, THAT'S BEING JUST LIKE ME! WHAT DO YOU HAVE TO SAY TO THAT?!

THIS IS FOR MILITARY MABEL.

EJECT

BOOOM!

AND SO...

WITH THIS SHIP WE CAN FIND OUR VARIOUS HOME DIMENSIONS! I CAN'T WAIT TO SEE MY DIPPER AGAIN!

THAT GLUE SEALED MY WOUNDS, SOLDIER! THANKS FOR EVERYTHING!

ME TOO!

ME THREE!

I'M A TABLE!

LATER, MABELS! DON'T DO ANYTHING I WOULDN'T DO! HAHA!

WELL, I GUESS WE'RE BOTH TERRIBLE CARETAKERS.

RESCUED BY OUR OWN NIECE.... I DON'T KNOW HOW WE'LL LIVE THIS DOWN.

HEY, FOR WHAT IT'S WORTH, I LOVE YOU BOTH.

BUT MAYBE THE REASON YOU TWO CAN'T TAKE CARE OF KIDS IS THAT YOU KINDA STILL *ARE* KIDS.

MAYBE IT'S TIME FOR YOU TO TAKE CARE OF EACH OTHER.

HAHA!

TAKE *THAT*, MULTIVERSE! THIS IS HOW WE DO IT IN *JERSEY!*

PINES! PINES! PINES!

I CAN'T BELIEVE YOU GOT TO GO TO THE MULTIVERSE! WHAT WAS IT LIKE?!

REAL STUPID, BUT THE STUPIDEST PART WAS ME. I GUESS WHAT I WANTED TO SAY IS...

I'M SORRY FOR BEING SELFISH THIS SUMMER.

I GUESS IT TOOK ME DEALING WITH *MYSELF* TO REALIZE WHAT YOU PUT UP WITH.

HAHA, OKAY, WHO ARE YOU AND WHAT HAVE YOU DONE WITH MABEL?

I SHOT HER OUT OF AN AIRLOCK.

OH...I ALSO GOT SOMETHING FOR YOU FROM SOMEONE NAMED *MABIPPER*.

SHE SAID I COULD HAVE IT.

SO DIPPER AND MABEL'S SUPERNATURAL SUMMER CAME TO A CLOSE. OF COURSE, THEY WEREN'T THE FIRST PINES TWINS TO GET INTO PARANORMAL TROUBLE.

I WAS ROOTING THROUGH STAN'S *"SECRETS DRAWER"* WHEN I FOUND THIS OLD SCRAPBOOK, WHICH HADN'T BEEN OPENED SINCE 1960-SOMETHING! YOU CAN STILL SMELL THE SALTWATER TAFFY!

IN IT, I DISCOVERED MANY FASCINATING THINGS, BUT MOST FASCINATING OF ALL WAS A TALE ABOUT THE *ORIGINAL* MYSTERY TWINS THAT HAD BEEN LOST TO TIME... UNTIL NOW.

A TALE I LIKE TO CALL...

ASBEST-O'S

GHASTLY GHOULS

GRANDPA THE KID
ADMIT ONE

SHUT YER YAP!

618618

SO I COME DOWN TO THE PAWNSHOP FOR A NICE DAY OF OVERCHARGING TOURISTS FOR BUFFALO NICKELS...

PINES PAWNS

JEWELRY WATCHES NO REFUNDS

AND WHAT DO I SEE?

AN ARCHAEOPTERYX?

BARF! LOTS OF BARF!

I FIND MY SWANKIEST GOLD CHAIN MISSING FROM ITS CASE!

WHAT? YOU SAYIN' *WE* DID THIS, PA?

NO, I'M SAYING *YOU* DID THIS, STANLEY!

FIRST YOU STOLE MRS. CRAMPELTER'S GLASS EYE. THEN THERE WAS YOUR "CRAB-FIGHTING RING."

YOU'RE ALWAYS PICKPOCKETING AND MONKEYSHINING, AND THIS IS THE LAST STRAW!

NO REFUNDS

BUT... BUT I'VE BEEN WITH STANFORD ALL DAY!

TELL 'IM, SIXER!

YEAH, PA. I KNOW STANLEY'S GOT A REPUTATION, BUT THIS TIME IT'S REALLY NOT HIM!

YOU REALLY WANNA STICK YOUR NECK OUT FOR GOOFUS OVER HERE? THEN PROVE IT, SMART GUY! YOU'VE GOT **24 HOURS** TO FIND THE CHAIN...

...OR STANLEY IS GONNA BE GROUNDED INDOORS FOR THE *REST OF THE SUMMER!*

MISSING:

GOLD CHAIN

REWARD
IF FOUND!
PUNISHMENT
IF NOT.

DARN, PA! I'M INNOCENT!

JEWELRY'S FOR GIRLS AND PIRATES! WHAT KINDA WEIRDO WOULD WANT THAT CHAIN ANYWAY?!

WAIT... *WEIRDO...*

THE JERSEY DEVIL!

FWIP FWIP FWIP

LEGEND HAS IT THAT THIS CLOVEN-HOOFED *WEIRDO* OF THE NIGHT HIDES BY THE BOARDWALK AND PILFERS GOLD AND JEWELS TO ADD TO ITS COLLECTION!

MANY HAVE HUNTED IT, BUT *NONE* HAVE LIVED TO TELL THE TALE.

ARE YOU SAYIN' THAT HORSE-FACED DONKEY-GOBLIN STOLE PA'S CHAIN?!

IF THE HOOF FITS... *LOOK!*

HOOFPRINTS! *HOT BISCUITS,* YOU MIGHT BE ON TO SOMETHING!

WE'RE GONNA FIND THAT MONSTER, GET THE CHAIN, AND GET BACK OUR SUMMER!

OKAY, TIME TO STOCK UP ON MYSTERY-HUNTING SUPPLIES AND WEAPONS!

WAY AHEAD OF YA! SAY HELLO TO MY ASSOCIATE...

SHANKLIN THE STAB POSSUM!

SCREEEE!

PART PET, PART ASSASSIN— THE PERFECT WEAPON!

PRIMITIVE, BUT EFFECTIVE.

ATTABOY, SHANKLIN! STAB THOSE MYSTERIES!

THUNK!

REEEEEEE

HISS!

DING! DING!

DID SOMEONE SAY MYSTERY?

WHO ARE *YOU*?

CREEPIN' COVE CAPTAINS! WE'RE THE *SIBLING BROTHERS*! AND NO ONE CRACKS A CAPER QUICKER THAN US!

AIN'T THAT RIGHT, *ASCOT*?

YOU BET YOUR LOAFERS, *DICKIE*! AND I'D SAY IT'S *TROUBLE O'CLOCK* AT CLUE COVE!

YIKES. YOU GUYS ALWAYS TALK LIKE THIS?

SURELY YOU'VE HEARD OF OUR CAPERS IN THE PAPERS!

WE'RE HERE TO SLEUTH THE SOCKS OFF THE *PECULIAR PUZZLE* OF THE *PURLOINED PAWNSHOP*!

MISSING: GOLD CHAIN

REWARD

WHAT? HEY, *BACK OFF!* THIS MYSTERY IS ALREADY OURS! WE CALLED IT FIRST!

SNICKER *YOU?*

MISSING:

NO OFFENSE, BUT IT MUST BE HARD TO STAY UNDERCOVER WHEN YOU HAVE *SIX FINGERS.*

AND YOUR BROTHER HAS A POSSUM IN HIS PANTS.

THAT'S *HIS HOME!* HE'S NESTING!

HIS SSS

SA

ERAL S

SORRY, CHUMS, BUT I DEDUCE THAT THERE'S ONLY ROOM IN THIS TOWN FOR *ONE* PAIR OF MYSTERY TWINS!

EXCELLENT DEDUCTION, DICKIE! SEE YOU IN THE FUNNY PAPERS!

SALE

HO HO

HO HO HO!

DON'T LISTEN TO THOSE JERKS! EVERYONE'S JEALOUS OF YOUR EXTRA FINGER!

AND I WILL *NEVER* APOLOGIZE FOR THIS PANTS POSSUM.

WE JUST NEED TO FIND THAT BEAST BEFORE THEY DO! ACCORDING TO THIS BOOK, CLUES COULD BE IN TWO PLACES...

PENNY ARCADE

EITHER HERE...

NOPE.

PEEP THE LADY

OH, MY!

SEE HER BLOOMERS

5¢

"OR..."

STEP RIGHT UP, FOLKS! SEE THE INCREDIBLE ONE-HEADED MAN! JUST A NICKEL TO SEE THE HUMAN PICKLE! WE'VE GOT SADDO, THE CLOWN THAT WON'T STOP CRYING! IT'S THE HAPPIEST PLACE IN JERSEY! NO COPS ALLOWED!

FREAK SHOW

FWOOOSH!

THIS SEEMS LIKE A GOOD PLACE FOR CHILDREN.

HEY, MUSCLES! YOU SEEN A MONSTER AROUND HERE?

SURE, EVERY TIME I LOOK IN THE MIRROR.

NOW, EITHER PAY TO LOOK AT WALRUS GIRL, OR GET LOST!

WE'RE NOT LEAVING UNTIL WE GET INFO ON THAT THING!

JERSEY D

WHERE IS IT HIDING?!

VERY WELL. WE WILL CONFIDE IN A FELLOW ABNORMAL ALLY.

LEGEND SAYS THE *JERSEY DEVIL* LIVES BY THIS VERY DOCK.

A CLUE TO ITS WHEREABOUTS WAS TATTOOED ON MY BACK BY A DRUNKEN SAILOR MANY YEARS AGO.

BUT I WAS NEVER ABLE TO CRACK THE RIDDLE...

"EAT SALTWATER JAFFE'S SEAGULL-FLAVORED TAFFY":

OH NO, SORRY. I RENT OUT THIS SHOULDER FOR ADS. LOOK BY MY SPINE.

"THE *HOUSE OF LIGHT* AT *SIX O'CLOCK*. A *PATHWAY HIDDEN* IN THE ROCKS. DESCEND BELOW THE *STONY STAIR*. YOU'LL FIND THE *DEVIL* LURKING THERE!"

A PATHWAY HIDDEN IN THE ROCKS

THE HOUSE OF LIGHT AT SIX O'CLOCK

DESCEND BELOW THE STONY STAIR

YOU'LL FIND THE DEVIL LURKING THERE

A HOUSE OF LIGHT...

WELL, I'M STUMPED!

THE *LIGHTHOUSE!* THAT'S IT!

BYE, KIDS!

SAY HI TO THE DEVIL FOR ME!

I LIKED THEM.

SSSSSORRY WE CALLED YOU NORMAL!

OKAY, LET ME DO ALL THE TALKING!

HEY, EYEPATCH! WE'RE GONNA RUMMAGE THROUGH YOUR *JUNK!*

LET US IN OR WE'LL CHUCK CRABS AT YER FACE!

HA! WHO DO YOU THINK YOU ARE, *THE SIBLING BROTHERS?!*

I AIN'T LETTIN' A KNOWN DELINQUENT LIKE STANLEY PINES IN HERE!

NOW *SCRAM* BEFORE I CALL THE AWKWARD TEENAGE LIFEGUARDS!

I DON'T GET IT, I SAID ALL THE RIGHT THINGS!

THERE'S GOT TO BE ANOTHER WAY TO—

OH, YOU GOTTA BE KIDDING ME!

OUTTA MY WAY, GRAMPS!

WHY, IT'S CLEARLY THE SIBLING BROTHERS, OR MY NAME AIN'T HORRIBLE EYESIGHT HAWKINS!

YEAH, YEAH. NOBODY ASKED YOUR LIFE STORY!

UGH, THIS SWEATER IS GIVING ME HIVES!

IF I EVER DRESS LIKE THIS ON PURPOSE, PUT BLEACH IN MY OVALTINE!

HMMM...IT'S SIX O'CLOCK, BUT I DON'T SEE ANY PATHWAY.

WAIT...

IF SIX O'CLOCK ISN'T A TIME... MAYBE IT'S AN ANGLE... 90 DEGREES OF ROTATION!

CHK

FLASH!

WWHRRRRRR

RRRRRR

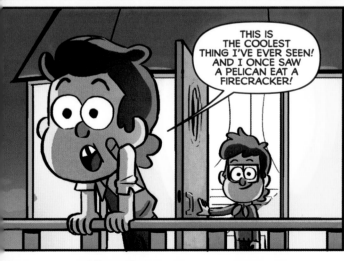

THIS IS THE COOLEST THING I'VE EVER SEEN! AND I ONCE SAW A PELICAN EAT A FIRECRACKER!

TO THE CAVE!

HEY, FORD... WHY DO YOU THINK PA IS SO HARD ON ME? DO YOU REALLY THINK I'M A BAD KID?

WHAT? NO, IT'S JUST...

YOU LIKE TAKING SHORTCUTS, AND SOMETIMES IT GETS YOU INTO TROUBLE, Y'KNOW?

SPLASH!

IT JUST SOMETIMES FEELS LIKE PA HATES ME.

OUR OLD MAN JUST HAS A SHORT FUSE. NO MATTER WHAT ANYONE SAYS, YOU'RE A GOOD KID, STANLEY.

HSSS

HEY!

COME BACK, SHANKLIN! YOU'RE ONLY SUPPOSED TO PICKPOCKET *STRANGERS!*

FLASH!

ALLOW US.

AUGH! YOU TWO!

WE HAVE SOMETHING YOU MIGHT WANT TO SEE.

UNLESS IT'S PICTURES OF YOU TWO GETTING KICKED BY A HORSE, I'M GOOD.

LOOK, BUSTER, WHILE YOU TWO WERE PLAYING DRESS-UP, WE JUST *SOLVED* THE CASE!

AND YOU *AIN'T* GONNA LIKE IT.

CLASSIFIED

WHAT... *STANLEY?!*

NO REFU

WE'VE GOT PHOTOGRAPHERS ALL OVER TOWN. HOW DO YOU THINK WE SOLVE EVERY MYSTERY?

LOOKS LIKE YOUR IDIOT BROTHER IS THE STICKY-FINGERED SCOFFLAW!

GALLOPING GUMSHOES, WHAT IS THAT?!

IT'S THE JERSEY DEVIL! IT'S REAL! I'D BE EXCITED IF I WASN'T SO TERRIFIED!

#@$!

HEY, HEY! LOOK WHO FINALLY LEARNED TO SWEAR!

AAUGHH!!

THUD!

HEY, LOOK, *HELL*!

WE'LL BE SAFE IN THERE!

WELCOME TO SATAN'S HELLHOLE

SCREECH!

SCRAW!

SCRAW!

SCREECH!

...

STANLEY...

WHY DID YOU STEAL PA'S CHAIN?!

I *TRUSTED* YOU!

I *DEFENDED* YOU!

I...

I DIDN'T STEAL IT, OKAY?! I WAS BORROWING IT! I WAS GONNA POLISH IT UP FOR PA AS A FATHER'S DAY GIFT!

BUT I ACCIDENTALLY SMASHED THE CASE AND GOT TOO SCARED AND EMBARRASSED TO TELL HIM WHAT HAPPENED!

NO MATTER WHAT I DO, I'M NOT A GENIUS LIKE YOU.

I'M A DUMB IDIOT WHO SCREWS EVERYTHING UP.

DO YOU KNOW WHAT IT'S LIKE BEING THE *STUPID TWIN*?

I WISH JUST ONCE PA WOULD LOOK AT ME THE WAY HE LOOKS AT YOU.

LIKE HE ACTUALLY *LIKES* ME.

STANLEY...

STOMP STOMP

FWIP!

THUD!

SCREE!

SCREE!

WELL, GUM MY SHOES, WHAT HAVE WE HERE?

LOOKS LIKE YOU'VE GOT A CHOICE, STANFORD.

YOU'VE ALWAYS WANTED TO CATCH A PARANORMAL BEAST—

AND WE'VE GOT ONE RIGHT HERE AT OUR FINGERTIPS!

GIVE US THE PHOTOS PROVING YOUR BROTHER'S GUILT AND WE'LL LET YOU KEEP THE MONSTER!

OTHERWISE, WE'LL FRAME YOU BOTH!

BUT PA WOULD NEVER FORGIVE ME!

LOOK, STANFORD, YOUR BROTHER MAY BE GUILTY, BUT YOU'RE NOT. WHY SHOULD YOU BE PUNISHED FOR THIS MORON'S CRIMES?

ONE DAY YOU'RE GONNA REALIZE THAT YOU'RE TOO GOOD FOR HIM.

DO YOU REALLY WANT YOUR BROTHER TO BE *DRAGGING YOU DOWN YOUR WHOLE LIFE*?

JOIN US OR GO DOWN TOGETHER!

SCREE...

FINE...I GUESS IT'S IMPORTANT TO ADMIT WHEN YOU'VE BEEN BESTED.

AND YOU'VE BEEN BESTED!

GET 'EM, SHANKLIN!

HISSSSS!

GNAW

GNAW

SCREECH!

FWOOSH!

AAAAH!

SPLASH!

SCREEEEEEE

HUFF...HUFF... YOU IDIOT! NOW NO ONE WILL KNOW YOU FOUND THE BEAST!

JUST WHO DO YOU TWO THINK YOU ARE?!

I'LL TELL YOU WHO WE ARE! WE'RE THE PINES TWINS, *KINGS OF NEW JERSEY!*

WE'RE WEIRDOS AND HOOLIGANS, AND WE LOOK OUT FOR EACH OTHER AND MISFITS LIKE US!

NOW GET OFF MY DOCK!

JUST YOU WAIT, WE'LL GET OUR REVENGE!

THERE'S NO ROOM IN THIS TOWN FOR FREAKS LIKE YOU!

OH YEAH?

WHO YOU CALLIN' FREAKS?!

"AND THAT'S HOW STANLEY AND ME WOUND UP GROUNDED FOR THE SUMMER.

STAN-O-WAR

"TO BE HONEST, WE DIDN'T EVEN MIND.

"SOLITARY CONFINEMENT ISN'T SO BAD WITH THE RIGHT PRISON MATE.

"PA WAS ANGRY WHEN STAN CONFESSED, BUT I THINK SOME SMALL PART OF HIM APPRECIATED THE HONESTY.

"I GUESS I'LL NEVER KNOW."

HEY, SIXER, YOU THINK WE'LL REALLY BE ADVENTURING FOR THE REST OF OUR LIVES?

ONLY TIME WILL TELL.

STAN-O'-WAR II

THE END

The Ballad of the Stan Bros

(to the tune of "Sailing, Sailing")
by Shmebulock the gnome

"Stanley, Stanford, over the bounding sea!
One was a brave adventurer, the other was Stanley!

Adventures, dentures,
They'll travel to foreign lands!

With fists and brains and bodily pains,
Nothing can stop the Stans!

SO THE STAN BROTHERS BEGAN AN ADVENTURE OF A LIFETIME, THE KIND OF ADVENTURE THAT WOULD MAKE A GREAT MOVIE, HONESTLY. MAYBE A MINISERIES? IS THAT TOO MUCH TO ASK?

HONESTLY, WOULD IT KILL THEM TO GIVE US SOME NEW ADVENTURES? AFTER SUMMER COMES FALL, A WHOLE NEW "SEASON," IF YOU WILL. I CAN'T BE THE ONLY ONE WHO WANTS ANOTHER *SEASON*, RIGHT? *RIGHT?!*

I'VE INVESTED SO MUCH TIME IN THESE CHARACTERS' LIVES, THEY CAN'T JUST LEAVE ME!

BY LUCIFER'S BEARD, WHAT WOULD IT TAKE FOR MORE GRAVITY FALLS?!

BUT I SUPPOSE ALL TALES MUST END. THERE IS AN OLD GNOMISH PROVERB, *"CGHA'KCK'URKLAAH,"* WHICH I BELIEVE TRANSLATES TO "EVERY SUNSET LEADS TO A SUNRISE." EITHER THAT OR THE GNOME WAS CHOKING ON A PINE CONE. PERHAPS IT IS TIME FOR ME TO STOP OBSERVING AND STARTING LIVING MY OWN STORIES.

BEFORE I RETURN TO MY PRISON OF SILENCE, I OFFER YOU ONE LAST SECRET—THERE IS A MESSAGE HIDDEN IN THIS BOOK, AND THE ONLY TRUE WAY TO FIND THAT MESSAGE IS...

SHMEBULOCK

THE END?

Soos's Comic Corner

'Sup, dudes? Soos here! FUN FACT: Did you know that comics are drawn not by gods but, in fact, by actual mortal human beings? It's true! Check out these rough sketches by the talented dawgs who made this comic a reality!

FACE IT

PRISCILLA TANG

Yikes! That face dude looks a lot better in the dark! I gotta wash my eyeballs after lookin' at that!

SCILLA TANG

PRISCILLA TANG

paper

gum

PRISCILLA TANG

PRISCILLA TANG

The writer and artist work together to brainstorm the most horrifying ideas possible. For the kids!

Sometimes the writer tries to draw, too! It's usually pretty embarrassing, dude!

ALEX HIRSCH

PRISCILLA TANG

Then the artist moves to pencil pages! Or as they're technically called in the comic industry, "scribbly bits."

Then the writer will add some notes. Usually small stuff like "Please add one billion more characters to every page."

Life ain't easy for Pacifica! I totally relate—being super good-looking has taken its toll on me, too!

COMIX UP

ASAF HANUKA

ASAF HANUKA

I'm geekin' out, dude! I want to get bitten by a radioactive talented person so I can draw like this!

ASAF HANUKA

Note the expertly rendered fat folds on my kneecap. Museum-worthy, dude!

Ever wonder what Dipper would look like if he had a nightmarish growth on his head? Wonder no more!

PRISCILLA TANG

PRISCILLA TANG

PRISCILLA TANG

PRISCILLA TANG

These glorious manga pages were drawn by the SAME ARTIST who drew "Face It"! I hope you're wearing a helmet, because I just blew your mind!

If you recognize these styles, bad news:
you're officially **old**, dude!

DON'T DIMENSION IT

These drawings are rough, but they have so much life and appeal! I wanna pinch that pig's cheeks!

Whoa!!
My condolences to this artist's wrist!

The secret to drawing Mabel: just draw Dipper and add longer hair, dude!

DID U NOTICE:
when little Ford puts on his jacket over the stolen red sweater, the classic "Ford look" is officially born! That little dude is a style icon, bro!

Sometimes pages are CUT for space— like this fun little interlude with the Pines boys doin' hijinks on the beach! They make New Jersey look fun!

Two more cut scenes: the Sibling bros comparing magnifying glass sizes with Ford— and a super-swole dude whaling on a clown!

The only thing scarier than the Jersey Devil is how much time it takes to draw comics. The REAL superheroes are behind the page!

JOE PITT

ANY THOUGHT FOR THIS REAL

JOE PITT

JOE PITT

tentacle should be on top of page border

Wanna know the secret to drawing this good? It's not taking off your shirt and rubbing this book all over your body. Trust me—I tried! It's hard work and practice! These artists all practice drawing every day and have made their comic dreams come tru If you wanna draw com you can do it, too, dude This is Soos Ramirez, and as I always say, if you ca staple it, it's a comic!

—Soos